PET HEALTH INSURANCE

A Veterinarian's Perspective

Bridging The Gap Between The Healthcare
Your Pet Needs and What You Can Afford

Dr. Doug Kenney

Cover by Jon Kenney: jon@jonkenney.com

Published by PhiloSophia Publishing
Memphis, Tn.
dr.dougkenney@yahoo.com

ISBN-13: 9780982322147
ISBN-10: 0982322143
Library of Congress Control Number: 2016948160

The information provided in this book was obtained as a result of my
personal research. While it is my goal to continually update this
information, things can change quickly in the pet insurance industry.
Before purchasing a pet insurance policy, confirm this information by
communicating with the pet insurance company and reading the most
recent policy available.

There are links to audio and video clips that will help you better
understand some of the concepts in this book. Some feature pet
insurance company representatives or stories from their policyholders.
These are provided for informational purposes only and should not
be considered an endorsement of those companies by the author.

** About the picture on the cover - Dr. Kenney is pictured with one
of his patients - Bentley, a Goldendoodle who is a therapy dog. You
can listen to a podcast episode where his owner discussed her research
process before choosing the company to insure Bentley and also how
the coverage came in handy when he accidentally ingested Ibuprofen.
http://tinyurl.com/gthrvpq

Table of Contents

Introduction

My journey to writing about pet insurance started several years ago when the only pet insurance company I knew existed was VPI. It had been around for about 25 years and we had a supply of their brochures on hand just in case a client asked about pet insurance.

On the way home one day, I stopped by a specialty hospital to check on a patient I had referred there earlier that afternoon. While waiting to talk with the internist, I saw a brochure about ASPCA pet insurance in the reception area. Soon thereafter, I received brochures from Pets Best and Embrace pet insurance. Both of these companies had just recently started up.

I started researching the industry and found that there were even more companies offering pet insurance. It had been easy to recommend a specific pet insurance company when the only one I knew about was VPI, but now I was aware of several other companies and their policies were all quite different.

I called and talked with company representatives and eventually established a relationship with at least one person who became my "go-to" contact at each company. Oftentimes, it was a veterinary colleague on staff at the company or the President/CEO of the company.

After reading reviews that pet owners posted online about their experiences with pet insurance, it became clear that those who had "buyer's remorse" weren't aware of all the options available to them when they purchased insurance or they simply didn't understand what they were buying. I realized that other pet owners and veterinarians probably had similar questions to those I had after visiting pet insurance company websites, so I decided to put what I'd learned into a book.

From my research, it was evident that pet insurance isn't a "one size fits all" product. Therefore, I also decided to forgo recommending a specific company because each pet owner has different needs and budgets when it comes to choosing a pet insurance company and policy to insure their pet. With a dozen or so pet insurance companies in the United States, there's enough variety to pick one that best fits your needs.

As a practicing veterinarian, I've often wondered why more pet owners don't have health insurance for their pets. I finally realized that they simply don't see what I see everyday. Unless they have been faced with a seriously injured or ill pet that required medical care that costs thousands of dollars, they simply don't see the need for it. Or, they believe that something like that will never happen to them.

Therefore, I've written this book from a veterinarian's perspective with insights into real life situations you should consider when deciding whether or not to purchase pet insurance. Who better to write a book on pet insurance than someone who diagnoses and treats the problems that pet owners will have to file claims for when their pet is sick or injured?

This book is written not only for those people who may have just recently heard about pet insurance and are investigating it for the first time, but also for those who may have looked at pet insurance in the past and decided that it was either too expensive or there were too many exclusions to be worthwhile. If that's the case, I urge you to take another look because there have been many changes in what's covered, and policies are now so customizable that you can almost always design a policy that meets your needs **and** fits your budget.

My goal for this book is to provide information for veterinarians and pet owners that is:

✓ Accurate and up-to-date.

✓ Easy to understand.

✓ Helpful when deciding if they should purchase pet insurance, and if so, which company and policy best fits their needs.

✓ Unique - not found anywhere else - including audio and video.

If you would be kind enough to let me know if I have achieved these goals for you, there is a free offer in the Resources chapter at the end of the book (pg.73) as a token of my appreciation. It has the potential to save you thousands of dollars on your pet's healthcare expenses over the life of your pet.

In the digital version of this book, there are links to audio and video clips to enhance the reader experience. You can have access to these audio and video clips even while reading this printed book through provided weblinks you can type into your internet browser or by scanning a QR code with the camera on your mobile phone or tablet.

There are several free QR readers available for both ios and android devices in the App store on your phone or tablet. My favorite on the iphone is the QR Code Reader & Barcode Scanner by MixerBox.

I encourage you to download one of these readers to your phone or tablet and keep it handy as you're reading this book. I think you will enjoy this additional content.

Is Pet Insurance For You?

If you are the typical person in America today, you probably have several different types of insurance. If you own a home, you likely have homeowners insurance. If you own a car, you likely have auto insurance. You may have life insurance, disability insurance, or health insurance. Why do you need all these types of insurance? Consider the following scenarios:

✓ If your house burned down, could you personally write a check to have it rebuilt?

✓ If you had a wreck and your car was dented, could you pay out-of-pocket to have it repaired? If it was totaled, could you purchase another comparable car?

✓ If you died or were disabled, would your family be able to carry on and pay all the bills without your income?

✓ If you became seriously ill and required surgery and an extended hospital stay and the bill was $100,000 - would you be able to pay it?

Most of us don't have the resources to pay for such unexpected and expensive events. Likewise, pet owners buy pet insurance to help them pay for large, unexpected veterinary bills that they would have trouble paying for out-of-pocket. The definition of "large" might be $500 for some pet owners while it may be $5000 or more for other pet owners.

Pet insurance transfers the risk of significant financial loss from the pet owner to the insurance company.

Pet healthcare expenses fall into two categories:

1) Wellness care e.g. annual or semi-annual examinations, vaccinations as needed, heartworm and intestinal parasite testing, heartworm preventative medication, flea and tick

control products, professional teeth cleaning and examination, wellness laboratory testing, microchipping, spaying or neutering, etc. You likely know about how much these costs are going to be every year and also when these procedures are due. Therefore, you can plan and save for them - they aren't unexpected.

2) Accidents or illnesses e.g. accidental poisoning, foreign body ingestion, fractures, lacerations, acute or chronic diseases, etc. These are, by nature, unplanned or unexpected and sometimes expensive – especially if treated at an emergency hospital or you are referred to a specialist. These expenses are why pet owners usually consider the purchase of pet insurance.

Pets Best pet insurance company reviewed their claims over $500 to determine where the pets were treated and found that:

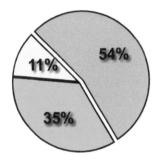

○	Regular Veterinarian
○	Specialty Hospital
○	Emergency Hospital

Therefore, if your pet experiences an unexpected and serious injury or illness, you have almost a 50% chance of being seen at an emergency hospital or being referred to a specialist.

Specialists have more advanced training and access to more advanced technology (e.g. CT scans or MRIs) to help them solve and treat the more difficult cases. Emergency hospitals often deal with life-threatening problems that need intensive care or even emergency surgery – usually at hours when your regular veterinarian's hospital isn't open.

For these reasons, the fees at specialty and emergency hospitals are usually higher than what you would pay at your regular veterinarian's hospital. Specialty and emergency hospitals play an important role, along with your primary care veterinarian, in providing quality healthcare for your pet, and (when needed) can be the difference between the successful or unsuccessful treatment of your pet.

Therefore, pet owners are starting to look more closely at pet insurance as a way to help bridge the gap between the quality of healthcare they need or want for their pet and what they can afford.

Surveys have been taken that asked pet owners how much they would spend to save their ill or injured pet. A large percentage of pet owners replied that they would be willing to spend "anything" to save their pet. It has been my experience, however, that when I present the cost of a diagnostic or treatment plan to pet owners, it's no longer a theoretical question on a survey – but reality, and some aren't so sure of the answer anymore.

Dr. Barry Kipperman, an internist at a California 24-hour emergency and specialty hospital, stated that he frequently hears pet owners say:

> "I never imagined it would cost this much to save my pet's life."

There have been instances when only a couple of months after purchasing health insurance for their pet, people have been faced with an accident or illness that costs several thousand dollars to treat. Watch this video http://tinyurl.com/zlvv8sc

Keep in mind also, as your pet ages, he or she will likely develop a treatable chronic disease. Watch this video http://tinyurl.com/hj29wjj.

A couple of pet insurance companies have told me that about 40% of the claims they process are for chronic, on-going conditions. The cumulative costs of treating these conditions for the life of the pet can easily amount to thousands of dollars. Chronic diseases aren't limited to just older pets. Some chronic diseases can develop in pets even less than a year old and require lifelong treatment. Look at the chart below (courtesy of Petplan pet insurance company) of actual claims they've paid for various chronic conditions:

Mattie, a 5-year-old West Highland White Terrier (Hazleton, PA)			
patella luxation and inflammatory bowel disease	**year 1** $5,751	**year 2** $6,220	**year 3** $2,691	**total** (so far) **$14,662**

Tigger, a 4-year-old mixed breed dog (Wyckoff, NJ)			
hip dysplasia	**year 1** $4,542	**year 2** $9,055	**year 3** $10,169	**total** (so far) **$23,767**

Oni, a 7-year-old domestic shorthair cat (Forest Hills, NY)			
cancer (lymphoma)	**year 1** $259	**year 2** $9,641	**year 3** $3,554	**total** (so far) **$13,454**

Maddie, a 4-year-old mixed breed dog (San Diego, CA)			
cruciate ligament disease with arthritis	**year 1** $3,572	**year 2** $7,718	**year 3** $6,331	**total** (so far) **$17,621**

Cody, a 2-year-old Soft Coated Wheaten Terrier (New Windsor, NY)			
food allergies	**year 1** $475	**year 2** $5,090	**year 3** $7,847	**total** (so far) **$13,412**

Lydia, a 10-year-old mixed breed dog (Austin, TX)			
cancer (anal gland adenocarcinoma)	**year 1** $4,461	**year 2** $2,898	**year 3** $7,739	**total** (so far) **$15,098**

The "total so far" column gives you an idea of potential cumulative costs associated with managing these conditions year after year. Fortunately these pets were insured early and these conditions were covered. If your pet develops a chronic condition prior to your purchasing pet insurance, it will be considered pre-existing and won't be covered. Then, you'll be faced with having to pay these costs out-of-pocket.

Watch these videos as pet owners tell their stories about how having pet insurance allowed them to say "Yes" when their pet faced an unexpected accident or illness:

Atlas is a Doberman who likes to eat things he shouldn't resulting in several surgeries to remove these foreign bodies at a substantial cost. http://tinyurl.com/gukat48

Benny started developing chronic problems at only 8 months of age (elbow dysplasia, bilateral ACL tears, allergies, infections) incurring substantial costs to the owner (over $40,000) of which over $33,000 has been reimbursed. There are also significant ongoing costs related to treating these conditions. http://tinyurl.com/jddsg71

Baxter developed inoperable cancer affecting his ability to walk. He underwent a relatively new radiation treatment called Cyberknife which improved his prognosis and quality of life tremendously. http://tinyurl.com/jqvjp6n

Arrow developed torsion of the lung at 3 years old requiring removal of 2 lung lobes, but now is getting back to his normal quality of life. http://tinyurl.com/gwx2s52

Daisy ate part of a baseball and had surgery to remove it, then developed complications requiring a second surgery and an extended hospital stay. Daisy's owners didn't have insurance at the time, but are big believers in pet insurance now. http://tinyurl.com/gr5hnk7

It's obvious the pets in these stories are valued members of the family. Do you feel the same way about your pet(s)? For some of you, your eyes were just opened to the things that can happen to pets and the costs involved in treating these problems. And don't assume something like that will never happen to your pet. The fact is - you simply don't know that.

Dr. Jason Nicholas (aka "The Preventive Vet") has worked in pet emergency hospitals and talked to many pet owners faced with having to spend thousands of dollars to save their pet. Are most pet owners prepared for these situations? Listen to what he has to say: http://tinyurl.com/zwpypox

So, here are two questions that can help you decide if pet insurance is for you:

1. How much would you be **willing** to spend to save your pet's life if there is a reasonable chance for a good quality of life after treatment?

2. How much would you be **able** to spend to save your pet's life if there is a reasonable chance for a good quality of life after treatment?

If the answer to the first question is greater than the answer to the second question, you should seriously consider the purchase of pet insurance. Sooner or later in your pet's lifetime, you are likely to be faced with having to spend hundreds to thousands of dollars to diagnose and treat a serious illness or injury.

Petplan claims data from 2010 revealed that:

Every year 1 in 3 pets require unexpected veterinary care.

Pets under 1 year of age are 2.5 times as likely to be subjects of insurance claims as pets of any other age (this is contrary to the notion many people have that young, seemingly healthy pets don't need to be insured).

40% of insured pets develop a chronic disease that lasts beyond 12 months.

Having your pet insured can allow you to say "yes" to the tests and procedures that are required for a diagnosis and treatment of these unexpected and often expensive conditions.

Who **doesn't** need to purchase pet insurance? If you are self-insured (you have the ability to pay any veterinary bill, small or large, out of pocket without going into debt), you don't need pet insurance. However, I can imagine even some of these individuals purchasing low premium catastrophic coverage. I've also had some clients over the years tell me flat out, "Doc, if it's going to cost more than $500, I'll just put him down and go get another dog." Folks that have this philosophy of pet ownership apparently don't consider their pet a valued member of the family and don't need to purchase pet insurance either.

I believe more and more pet owners will purchase pet insurance in the future because technology and the costs of delivering quality healthcare to pets have outpaced the ability of many pet owners to pay for it. Consequently, veterinarians and pet owners will have to become familiar with pet health insurance. While pet owners and veterinarians alike can benefit from third party payment to help pay for the healthcare of pets, I'm convinced the real winners will be the pets.

Putting An End To Economic Euthanasia

 Dr. Jack Stephens, a veterinarian, had a life-changing encounter while shopping in a grocery store with his wife. Turning down the aisle, Dr. Stephens met a client and her daughter. Upon greeting, the client said to her daughter, "Honey, you remember Dr. Stephens don't you?" Her reply was, "Yes, he's the man who killed my dog."

Some weeks previously Dr. Stephens euthanized their pet, at the mother's insistence, because the family was unwilling or unable to spend the necessary funds to diagnose and treat the ill pet. It seems the daughter blamed him for the death of her beloved pet.

Shocked at the response from his client's daughter, Dr. Stephens resolved then and there to do something about "economic euthanasia" - embarking on a lifelong quest to provide pet owners with a method to always be able to afford their pet's care.

He founded and operated the first successful pet insurance company in the United States (VPI) in 1982. He left the company in 2004, and in 2005 founded another pet insurance company, Pets Best. He retired as President of the company in 2014, but remains active in the industry.

Whenever you are faced with the decision about whether to go forward with treatment when your pet has a serious illness, you want the decision to be based on prognosis for recover and quality of life rather than finances.

Dr. Barry Kipperman (mentioned earlier) believes that economic euthanasia is preventable - just like many other diseases that veterinarians see everyday. Listen as he explains:
http://tinyurl.com/pmhaor8.

Listen as Dr. Kerri Marshall, a veterinarian, talks about how pet insurance can help solve the problem of economic euthanasia.
http://tinyurl.com/nwu4kqu

Listen as Dr. John Faught, owner of Firehouse Animal Health Center in Austin, Texas describes the scenario where he's seen pet insurance make the decision whether to treat or euthanize a pet easier for pet owners: http://tinyurl.com/zrpun9h

Listen as Dr. Darlene Cook tells how pet insurance has come in handy with her own pet's healthcare expenses:
http://tinyurl.com/j8sdlmm

Listen as Jeannie Dardano, pet insurance liaison at a 24 hour Emergency and Specialty Hospital in Denver, talks about the cost of care and sadly the reality that pet owners opt for euthansia when they can't afford the treatment their pet needs.
http://tinyurl.com/hyxrev3

Pet Health Savings Account or Pet Insurance?

One bit of advice that I see over and over on the internet is to open a savings account to help pay for your pet's healthcare needs rather than buying pet insurance. The recommendation is to put the money you would "waste" on pet insurance premiums into the savings account, and when you have to go to the vet, the money will be there to pay for the visit (and it's your money).

People who give this advice miss the point of pet insurance. I think it's great advice to have a savings account, but not *instead of* pet insurance. Pet insurance helps you bridge the gap financially when the unplanned and unexpected occur *before* you have adequate savings in reserve. Your savings can also help you pay for annual wellness expenses and your deductible, co-pay and for any uncovered expenses if you have pet insurance.

Listen to my conversation with Dr. Carol McConnell, the Chief Veterinary Medical Officer at Veterinary Pet Insurance (VPI), a Nationwide Company. http://tinyurl.com/poypo4u

Dr. Fran Wilkerson of Pet Insurance University explains why insurance is different from an investment and how pet insurance can be a vital part of maintaining your financial health: http://tinyurl.com/olfbr5u

Laura Bennett, the CoFounder and CEO of Embrace pet insurance company talks about the importance of pet owners having a plan in place that includes both pet insurance and a savings account to help pay for their pet's healthcare expenses: http://tinyurl.com/hlh3zz7

Watch this video as a pet owner explains the value of pet insurance over just a savings account alone. http://tinyurl.com/ztxw94p

People who purchase pet health insurance must understand there will be years when they pay the premium and realize little to no benefit from the policy (don't have to file a claim). This is actually good! That means your pet remained healthy that year. It's this way with almost any other type of insurance too. Remember, the purpose of buying insurance is to protect you against catastrophic events that *may* occur in your life that you aren't able to financially cover yourself. You should no more buy pet health insurance hoping your pet will get sick than you'd buy auto insurance hoping you'll have a wreck.

Tom Collins wrote an excellent article for BlogPaws that sums up the purpose and benefit of having pet insurance for your pet. Here's his conclusion:

"You're buying protection against a disaster you hope will never happen and the peace of mind you'll have in knowing that if it does, your pet's health - or even survival - will not depend on how big your savings account has gotten."

Listen as Sebastiaan, who insured all five of his cats, explains what I believe is the right philosophy about pet insurance:
http://tinyurl.com/jcebfdh

Since it's inception in the United States in 1982, pet insurance has operated according to a reimbursement model. The pet owner pays their veterinarian, files a claim, and gets reimbursed by the insurance company. Many pet owners use a credit card to pay their veterinarian and then promptly file a claim with the insurance company. When the time comes to pay the credit card bill, they should have already received a reimbursement check from the insurance company.

Some of our clients have a CareCredit card that they use exclusively for their pet's medical expenses. CareCredit offers several no-interest payment plans that would work well with pet insurance. Just be sure to pay off the balance before the no-interest period expires to avoid high interest charges being added to your balance.

Here's a link to the CareCredit website:
(http://www.carecredit.com/vetmed)

Most pet owners will benefit from having a 3-pronged approach to paying for their pet's healthcare - savings, available credit, and pet insurance.

Listen as Dr. Jason Nicholas talks about being financially prepared for unexpected accidents and illnesses: (http://tinyurl.com/zxwscle)

Keep in mind that the best time to start saving, apply for CareCredit, and purchase pet insurance is *now* – before the unexpected happens. Since pet insurance policies don't cover pre-existing conditions and there is usually a waiting period before a policy becomes effective, after your pet gets sick or injured is too late for that particular problem to be covered by insurance. If it turns out to be an ongoing, chronic problem, it will never be covered. I've had plenty clients tell me they wished they had purchased pet insurance earlier.

Understanding Maximums, Deductibles and Coinsurance

Pet insurance policies have evolved over the past 10 years or so to allow pet owners to customize their policy by choosing a policy maximum, deductible and copay that results in a premium that fits their budget. Some companies also offer optional coverages that can be added for an additional premium as a "rider."

These are the common terms you'll see in pet insurance policies and it's very important you understand what each means and how it works:

✓ per-incident, annual, or lifetime maximum limits
✓ deductible – either per-incident or annual
✓ coinsurance or copay

Per-incident limit generally means the maximum the insurance company will pay out each time a new problem or disease occurs. Annual limit means the maximum the company will pay out during the policy term (usually one year). Generally, policies are renewable each year and the annual maximum benefit starts all over again. Some companies also have a lifetime limit that is the maximum the company will pay out during the pet's lifetime.

Whether your policy has an annual maximum, per-incident maximum or both can significantly affect your out-of-pocket expense. For example, if your pet gets sick with pancreatitis and your policy has a $10,000 annual limit and no per-incident limit, the company would pay out up to the full $10,000 for the illness. However, if your policy has a $10,000 annual limit and a $1500 per-incident limit, the company would pay out only up to $1500 for the illness and $8500 would be available for accidents or illnesses other than pancreatitis.

Therefore, if you end up purchasing a policy that has a per-incident limit, you should get the highest per-incident limit that you can afford. A general guideline, however, would be to avoid a policy with per-incident limits.

This table illustrates reimbursement of a $5,000 claim for a policy with and without a per-incident limit:

	Company A	Company B
Annual Maximum	$10,000	$10,000
Per-Incident Maximum	$1,500	None
Invoice Amount	$5,000	$5,000
Deductible	$100	$100
Copay 10%	$490	$490
You Pay	$3,500	$590
Company Pays	$1,500	$4,410

The deductible is what the pet owner is responsible for before the company will pay for anything. Some deductibles are per-incident and some are annual.

With a per-incident deductible, you will pay it each time your pet is examined for a new condition. For example, if your dog has a skin problem, an ear infection, a bite wound and an episode of vomiting during the policy year, you would pay a deductible for each problem. However, if you took your pet in for a skin problem and you had to take him back for several recheck visits, you would not have to pay another deductible for that problem.

Sometimes a per-incident deductible is called a "per-condition" deductible. You have to look closely at how the insurance company defines and applies this type of deductible - especially for chronic, ongoing conditions. It might mean that once you pay a deductible for that condition, you'll never have to pay a deductible again for the lifetime of the pet for that particular condition. This is nice for chronic conditions. However, some companies' per-incident/per condition deductible renews annually and you have to pay it again in subsequent years for each condition that is on-going, so it's like having an annual, per-incident deductible. If your pet has several chronic conditions, this can increase your out-of-pocket costs significantly and become annoying.

If your policy has a $100 annual deductible, then once you have spent $100 during that policy year on covered care, subsequent veterinary bills won't be subject to a deductible until your policy renews for the next policy year. Notice the potential out-of-pocket expense with an annual deductible compared to a per-incident deductible:

$100 Annual Deductible with 10% Coinsurance

Date	Reason for visit	Invoice Amount	Deductible	Copay	You pay	Insurance Reimburse
1/13	Diarrhea	$117	$100	$ 1.70	$101.70	$15.30
3/2	Broken nail	$104	None	$10.40	$10.40	$93.60
3/12	Recheck broken nail	$46	None	$4.60	$4.60	$41.40
6/30	Ear infection	$142	None	$14.20	$ 14.20	$127.80
Totals →		$409	$100	$30.90	$130.90	$278.10

$100 Per-Incident Deductible with 10% Coinsurance

Date	Reason for visit	Invoice Amount	Deductible	Copay	You pay	Insurance Reimburse
1/13	Diarrhea	$117	$100	$1.70	$101.70	$15.30
3/2	Broken nail	$104	$100	$0.40	$100.40	$3.60
3/12	Recheck broken nail	$46	None	$4.60	$4.60	$41.40
6/30	Ear infection	$142	$100	$4.20	$104.20	$37.80
Totals →		$409	$300	$10.90	$310.90	$98.10

Deductibles usually range from $0 to $1000. The lower deductible you chose, the higher your premium will be. If you are able and willing to be responsible for more of the bill yourself and select a higher deductible, your premium will be lower. However, when purchasing a policy with a per-incident deductible, you'll likely want to keep it as low as possible. Generally, an annual deductible is preferable because it is more predictable and easier to budget for.

Co-pay (also referred to as coinsurance) is the *percentage of the total bill* that the pet owner is responsible for. Therefore, it varies depending on the size of the invoice (claim). In contrast, the deductible is a fixed, known amount regardless of the total bill. Copays usually range from 0% to 30%. Notice the difference the copay can make in how much you have to pay out-of-pocket.

Invoice Amount	Deductible	Copay %	Copay	You pay
$3,000	$100	0%	$0	$100
$3,000	$100	10%	$290	$390
$3,000	$100	20%	$580	$680
$3,000	$100	30%	$870	$970

The lower the co-pay, the higher the premium will be. Several companies subtract the copay before subtracting the deductible. This results in a slightly lower reimbursement to the pet owner.

A popular Google search phrase on the internet is "cheap pet insurance." I assume that the person is searching for a pet insurance policy with the lowest possible premium. However, that's the wrong figure to look at when purchasing pet insurance for your pet. The most important figure to consider is your potential out-of-pocket costs (including the premium) if you have to file a large claim e.g. $5,000 or $10,000. In this instance, a policy with a low premium (lower annual or per-incident maximum, higher copay and/or higher deductible) could end up costing you significantly more out-of-pocket than a policy with a higher premium.

Therefore, never select a policy based solely on the lowest premium. Choosing the right policy maximum, deductible, and copay can literally save you thousands of dollars over the lifetime of your pet.

What You Need To Know About Premiums

What are the factors that pet insurance companies use to calculate premiums?

✓ Geographic location - Where you live affects the premium you will pay to insure your pet. For example, pet insurance premiums are generally higher in California than in Tennessee because veterinary fees are typically higher in California than Tennessee.

✓ The breed of your pet - Certain breeds of dogs or cats are known to have more health problems than other breeds, so premiums are higher for these breeds.

✓ The age of your pet - The older your pet is when you purchase pet insurance, the higher the premium will be because older pets generally have more health problems than younger pets. Older pets tend to develop chronic diseases that will need ongoing treatment. Not all pet insurance companies raise premiums just because your pet gets older, but some do and the increase can be substantial when a pet hits about 10 - 12 years old.

✓ Internal actuarial data - This is basically a company's claims experience that is unique to the pets insured by their policyholders.

In recent years, policyholders of several companies have opened their renewal notices to find their premiums were increasing significantly while others had their premiums actually decrease some. This topic is hardly ever talked about, but I believe it is essential for pet owners to have at least a basic understanding of it. So, I'm going to give you some information you won't find anywhere else to help you.

Recently, I asked Dr. Jack Stephens to write a guest blog post dealing with this issue. It's definitely worth the read because of his experience in the industry: http://tinyurl.com/o8la4w2

I also recently interviewed Laura Bennett, the CEO of Embrace pet insurance company, about premium increases in the pet insurance industry. The timing was relevant because Embrace had just adjusted their premiums. She is an actuary and explains very plainly all the factors used to determine what the new premims would be for their policyholders. Listen to pertinent portions of that interview: http://tinyurl.com/zsnup8h

How To Get Comprehensive Coverage At A Premium You Can Afford

As mentioned earlier, many of the companies allow you to customize your policy by giving you choices of the policy maximums, deductibles and copays as well as other optional coverages.

When customizing a policy, I suggest the following guidelines prioritized in this order:

Get the highest annual maximum you can afford. You are buying pet insurance primarily for that worst case scenario - a large expense.

Get the lowest copay you can afford. Remember that the copay is a percentage of the *total* bill and you'll pay it for every claim you file (unless your plan has 100% reimbursement) even if you've already met your deductible.

Get the lowest deductible you can afford, especially if it's a per-incident deductible. However, if you can afford a higher deductible, your premium will be lower. This is the first variable to adjust when trying to get a premium you can afford.

Your pet insurance premiums will go up over time whether due to the age of your pet, inflation, or when a company makes periodic adjustments based on its actuarial data. It may eventually get to the point where it exceeds your budget (comfort zone). When this happens, rather than canceling your policy, contact the company and ask about options to help decrease your premium. For example:

✓ Are you taking advantage of all the discounts the company offers?

✓ Are there riders for optional coverages that you don't need anymore. Sometimes it might make more sense to eliminate these before downgrading.

✓ You can downgrade your policy (raise the deductible and/or copay or decrease the annual maximum) to keep the premium within your budget.

Pet insurance companies generally allow you to downgrade a policy without your pet undergoing underwriting again. This means that any conditions your pet has been diagnosed with previously won't be considered pre-existing.

Conversely, if you upgrade your policy (lower the deductible or copay or raise the annual maximum), your pet may be subject to underwriting and any conditions previously diagnosed may not be covered. Or, perhaps previous conditions for which you've filed claims will be covered at the old limits and not the new limits of the upgraded policy.

So, generally, it would be better to start with the best policy you can afford and downgrade later if needed to keep the premium within your budget.

If your premium increases out of your comfort zone, you'll need to look at several combinations of a higher deductible, copay, or lower annual maximum that yields a premium you can afford. Then compare your out-of-pocket costs (including the premium) for each of these combinations should you have to file a large claim. This process will help you select the best way to downgrade your policy.

Pet insurance companies ought to inform policyholders of several options to lower their premium whenever they send out renewal notices with premium increases. Ideally, they should include what your new premium would be with each option. Then you can calculate what your out-of-pocket expense would be (including the premium) with each option should you have to file a large claim.

If your pet is already being treated for one or more chronic conditions, then you know what the likely cost of the treatment and monitoring (recheck exams and testing) will be based on the past year. Plugging these costs into your calculations can help you decide which scenario is best for your unique situation.

A reader of my blog recently contacted me when his premium increased 30% for his 13-year old dog. His policy already had the highest per-incident deductible the company offered and he really liked his 0% copay. His dog had several chronic conditions that require periodic exams, testing and medications. After doing some calculations, he decided to lower his policy maximum by several thousand dollars annually (he'd never come close to reaching the maximum in a policy year before) and stick with the 0% copay. During the subsequent year, his dog developed another major problem that caused him to exceed the annual maximum of the downgraded policy. So, downgrading the policy maximum ended up costing him more out of pocket than anticipated.

So, be careful when lowering the policy's annual maximum because you want your policy to cover that worst-case-scenario above all else. Several pet insurance companies have a "no annual limits" policy to eliminate this concern.

Be sure to verify what your new premium will be with a company representative based on the changes you'd like to make. Seek their help and advice, but always do the math yourself to make sure you're making the best decision.

The Policy Selection Worksheet, one of the tools in the Pet Insuance Toolkit, is good to use when your premium rises and you are considering downgrading your policy to get a premium closer to your comfort zone. All you have to do is plug in the policy maximum, deductible, copay, and premium and your out-of-pocket costs are automatically calculated for you for varios sized claims.

The toolkit is available at: http://petinsurancetoolkit.com

Choosing A Company To Insure Your Pet

When choosing a pet health insurance company, you are starting a relationship that you need to be comfortable with. The best one for you may not be the best one for someone else. Sometimes the service you receive and the trust factor is more important than the cost factor. Because pre-existing conditions are not covered by any insurance company, it is best if you make the right choice the first time rather than being dissatisfied and switching later to another company after you've filed several claims. By then, your pet may have one or more conditions that won't be covered because they are considered pre-existing with the new company.

Most Important Factors To Consider

Despite what you may think, the premium isn't the most important thing to consider when evaluating and comparing pet insurance companies. Your focus should be on what a policy covers. These are the factors from my perspective as a veterinarian that I consider the most important:

Coverage for hereditary conditions.

These are problems that your pet may be prone to develop because of known inherited problems in certain breeds e.g. hip dysplasia in some large breed dogs, luxating patellas (dislocating kneecaps) in some small breed dogs, idiopathic epilepsy (seizures) in Beagles or polycystic kidneys in Persian cats. There are websites that lists hereditary conditions in dogs and cats.

Dogs: (http://tinyurl.com/hcmu2pp)

Cats: (http://tinyurl.com/ntl2mgk)

I have seen instances where the insurance company considered a condition hereditary and the veterinarian did not, but unfortunately the insurance company's opinion is the one that counts and the claim was rejected. In order to avoid this situation, buy a policy from a company that covers hereditary conditions.

Listen as Laura Bennett, CEO of Embrace explains why coverage for hereditary conditions is so important: http://tinyurl.com/jgmzv3o

Coverage for chronic conditions.

These are diseases that cannot be cured, but may be treated and controlled so that your pet may live several more years with minimal symptoms and a good quality of life. This is an important consideration because virtually all dogs and cats, if they live long enough, will eventually develop a chronic condition e.g. diabetes, heart failure, kidney failure, Cushings disease, arthritis, hypothyroidism, hyperthyroidism, or cancer. With any chronic condition, there will be some ongoing diagnostics and treatment for the rest of the pet's life. Sometimes these costs can be significant.

Listen as Laura Bennett, CEO of Embrace talks about coverage for chronic conditions: http://tinyurl.com/z9w38xv

How reimbursements are calculated

This could affect how much reimbursement you get back from the company. Here are the 3 ways pet insurance companies calculate reimbursements at this time:

- ✓ Pays according to whatever the veterinarian charges on your invoice. This is generally the most predictable.

- ✓ Pays according to a benefit schedule that shows the maximum annual amount the company will pay for listed conditions/illnesses.

- ✓ Pays according to what is considered usual, reasonable, and customary for your region of the country.

The reason there may be a difference between what an insurance company considers usual and customary and what your veterinarian charges is that the actual costs of delivering care may vary from one practice to another - even in the same city. There are a number of variables that go into how a veterinary practice sets its fees. For example, some practices may have a larger hospital, more staff, more advanced equipment, and handle more difficult medical and surgical cases. Other practices may not have some of this equipment, and instead refer cases needing certain diagnostic procedures, surgeries, etc. to a specialist.

Generally, reimbursing a percentage of the veterinary invoice (whatever the veterinarian charges) results in higher payments to the policyholder. This may also be an attempt by some of the newer companies to simplify the reimbursement process so it is more understandable and predictable for veterinarians and pet owners alike. At the same time, it remains to be seen if these companies can stay competitive (keep their premiums affordable) while taking this approach.

Customer reviews/ratings of the companies

If you are like me, before you buy almost anything of significance, you look at customer reviews. Here you will read about the experiences of people who have actually purchased the product and/or dealt with the company. You will learn things by doing this that you won't learn on the company's website or even reading this book. I would advise you to not purchase a health insurance policy for your pet without looking at some reviews.

Coverage for alternative therapy

These are things like acupuncture or chiropractic treatments, homeopathic or holistic treatments, etc. These are becoming more popular with pet owners and some veterinarians are becoming certified to administer these treatments. Always ask, "What are the limits of coverage?"

Coverage for behavioral therapy

These are things like separation anxiety, noise phobias (thunderstorms or July 4th fireworks), litterbox aversion, aggression, obsessive-compulsive disorders, etc. Behavior problems are among the most common reasons that pets are relinquished to shelters and otherwise healthy pets are euthanized. Ideally, these disorders are better prevented than treated, but there are veterinarians who specialize in diagnosing and treating behavior disorders. Again, ask, "What are the limits of coverage?"

Coverage for dental diseases

Preventative therapy such as teeth cleaning and examination by a veterinarian under anesthesia is very important to your pet's overall health. Coverage for this procedure can be obtained by purchasing a wellness care plan (usually offered as a rider) from those companies that offer it.

Most companies will cover fractured teeth because of an accident. However, you should ask if the company covers extraction of these teeth only or will it also cover a root canal and/or crowns. If possible, it is better to save teeth considered to be strategic (e.g. canine teeth) rather than extracting them - especially in hunting or working dogs.

Does the company cover treatment of periodontal disease? This is the most common disease seen in pets. Some companies don't cover it because they consider it preventable (ideally by brushing your pet's teeth several times a week and regular dental checkups). I agree that in theory it is preventable, but practically - not so much. Some companies do cover periodontal disease, but be careful to ask exactly what they cover and don't cover in the treatment of this disease.

Does the company cover treatment of FORLs (feline oral resorptive lesions or tooth resorption) in cats? Dr. Barden Greenfield, a veterinary dental specialist (listen to audio clip below), believes that this is not a preventable disease and is common in cats - therefore it should be covered.

Does the company cover feline gingivitis/stomatitis complex?

Coverage for dental diseases is "all over the map" and because they are common in pets, you should determine how a company covers these problems by reading a sample policy and/or contacting the company directly and asking these questions.

Listen to my conversation with Dr. Greenfield (aka. "Your Pet Dentist) at Memphis Veterinary Specialists as he discusses the most common dental diseases in both dogs and cats, how they are usually treated, and the costs of these treatments. He believes that pet insurance can help you manage these costs and allow you to say "yes" to the best treatment for each problem should your pet ever be diagnosed with one of these diseases: http://tinyurl.com/jquuk35

Coverage for prescription diets

I include this because veterinarians sometimes use these diets as a "test" when doing a hypoallergenic food trial to rule out a food allergy. Many of these prescription diets are specially formulated to help control/treat certain diseases. While it is unrealistic to expect a company to cover the full costs of these foods, some do cover a percentage of the cost up to a maximum dollar amount annually and/or length of time.

Will the company pay the veterinary hospital directly?

The current model for pet insurance is reimbursement - you pay your vet up front for the full amount of the bill, then file a claim to get reimbursed. But, what if you have a very large bill and you can't afford to pay the full amount up front? Some companies will pay the veterinarian directly while you would pay the deductible, copay, and for any items not covered under the terms of the policy (assuming your veterinarian will accept such an arrangement). See later chapter on the future of pet insurance (pg. 65).

Coverage for wellness care

This includes things such as wellness exams, vaccinations, heartworm testing, heartworm preventative, flea preventatives, teeth cleaning, wellness testing, spaying or neutering, etc. In my opinion, preventative care through your veterinarian ought to be relatively inexpensive and something you can handle yourself financially. Many of these procedures are elective and/or they can be planned and saved for in advance. In fact, you are probably already paying for this out of pocket. See later chapter on wellness coverage (pg. 51).

Keep in mind that the primary reason for buying pet health insurance is coverage for unexpected accidents and illnesses for which you would have trouble paying for out of pocket in the event of a large claim. This is why I recommend selecting a company and policy based first and foremost on their coverage of accidents and illnesses.

Coverage for examination fees

Some companies don't cover your costs for examination fees (or make it optional). This is almost like another deductible when your pet is examined. If you are comfortable with that and pleased with the other aspects of a policy - okay - you just need to be aware of this.

These costs can add up if your pet is hospitalized for several days and examined one or more times each day - especially if it is at a specialty hospital, or if your pet has a condition that requires several recheck exams to monitor progress and treatment.

Getting Started - Doing Research In 5 Easy Steps

It can seem like a daunting task to choose one company from the dozen or so companies selling pet insurance in the United States. So, where do you start? How do you go about comparing companies so you make a wise choice?

In the picture below, you see one tree that stands out from the rest. I recommend a 5-step method of researching and comparing companies with the goal that one company will stand out from the rest as you make your choice of a company to insure your pet.

You should be able to eliminate several companies with each step so that by the time you get to Step 4, you should be down to only 2 or 3 companies to choose from. Therefore, you should complete Step 1 for all the companies before going on to Step 2, and then Step 2 for all the companies not eliminated in Step 1 before going on to Step 3, etc.

Step 1 - Get A Quote

Getting a free quote is easy - it's usually very prominently displayed on each company's home page.

There are some things you'll learn about each company's policies only when you get a quote.

You should get a quote from <u>all</u> the companies that insure pets in the United States. Only by getting a quote from all the companies will you know you've looked at every available option for you and your pet. In fact, one of the most common regrets that pet owners express when writing reviews is that they weren't aware they had other options when they chose a company. Be sure to save and/or print your quote.

When you obtain a quote, some companies may "recommend" a policy to you or reveal which policy is the "most popular." Be very careful about accepting their recommendation without critical thinking on your part. I've seen some companies recommend a less expensive policy (likely because the premium is more competitive) that would leave the pet owner paying most of the bill out-of-pocket if a large claim is filed. Use the guidelines I previously recommended when getting a quote to select a policy with the best coverage possible that's also within your budget (pgs. 30-31).

Another thing you should be aware of when getting a quote - sometimes companies won't show all the policy maximums, deductibles, copays, or other options (riders or endorsements) on their quote page. I've inquired why and was told that too many options tend to confuse people when they are getting a quote. However, not revealing all the options on their website limits the number of ways you can customize a policy and could result in your not getting the best coverage you can afford. Therefore, if you are having trouble customizing a policy to suit your needs, call the company to inquire if there are other options that aren't shown on their website. For example always ask, "Is this the highest annual maximum you offer?"

Since there is so much variation in policies from company to company, it is virtually impossible to compare apples to apples and oranges to oranges. The only variable that you can absolutely control and keep comparable from company to company while doing your research is the premium. Therefore, to more accurately compare companies with one another, I recommend 2 guidelines to use when obtaining a quote from each company:

1. Select a premium amount (range) you would be comfortable paying and/or fits your budget (e.g. $30-$45/mo.).

2. Select a policy that doesn't cover wellness care because all the companies don't offer this coverage.

After selecting the 4 or 5 companies with the best accident/illness coverage for your pet, if you decide you want to get wellness coverage, you can select any companies among these that also offers wellness coverage. However, you may find that the company with the very best accident/illness coverage for your pet doesn't offer wellness care coverage. Then, you'll have to decide just how important wellness coverage is to you while keeping in mind that the primary reason for purchasing pet insurance should be coverage for unexpected accidents and illnesses.

You also need to know what the expectations are for premium increases as your pet gets older when choosing a company - especially if insuring a young pet. Premiums for younger pets are fairly low and similar from company to company, but you might be shocked at the disparity in premiums for older pets from company to company. Not all companies raise premiums as a pet ages, but many do. Therefore, getting a quote for your pet at 7 and 10+ years old may allow you to eliminate even more companies before going on to the next step.

Step 2 - Read Reviews

Watch this short video where I interview the owner of the best review website for pet insurance companies (IMHO) as he explains how to use his site: http://tinyurl.com/hwb35hw

While reading reviews, keep in mind that some of the negative experiences people have had (and some admit it) are because they didn't do their research before purchasing a policy.

Look at the dates of the reviews and read the comments/follow-ups that are written after a review. Sometimes a company will update or improve their policies. You want to know if problems that pet owners have had in the past with a company are still occurring after an update. Consider printing out the most helpful reviews.

Listen to Laura Bennett, Embrace's CEO talk about the importance of reading reviews: http://tinyurl.com/hglwsf4

Step 3 - Read A Sample Policy

Read every word. You will find things in the policy that you won't find in this book or on the company's website. Consider the policy you'll sign a legal contract between you and the insurance company and you shouldn't ever sign a contract without reading and understanding it. Unfortunately, some people only take time to actually read their insurance policy after a claim is denied because of an exclusion that they weren't aware of. Some of the negative reviews on the review site illustrate this. If you are able to print the policy, you can highlight areas of the policy that you have questions about and call the company to get answers to those questions.

One thing to pay attention to is the waiting periods for various conditions. Some companies have longer waiting periods e.g. 6 months or a year for certain orthopedic conditions or intervertebral disk disease (slipped disk), etc. Sometimes they will waive the longer waiting period if you have your pet examined by your vet and no evidence of these conditions is found. So, don't get caught by surprise by this.

Listen to Dr. Fran Wilkerson's comments about the importance of reading a sample policy: http://tinyurl.com/zvsyb2a

Even after you sign up for pet insurance and receive your policy - read it again to make sure it is indeed what you understood you bought. The policy will usually have a "Declarations Page" where the company will show a summary of your coverage and any exclusions based on the information you provided the company about your pet when you signed up and/or a review of your pet's medical records.

Be aware of any requirements (e.g. exam by a veterinarian) to maintain coverage. Sometimes longer waiting periods on certain conditions can be waived if examined by a veterinarian within a certain length of time after signup.

Start a file where you keep this policy along with all other correspondence with the pet insurance company and all your veterinary invoices.

Step 4 - Call and/or Email Company

When you purchase pet insurance, you are starting a relationship with the company and it's representatives. By calling and emailing each company, you'll get a sense of their responsiveness and customer service. I have talked to pet owners who said that this was the deciding factor after they had narrowed down their search to 2 or 3 companies. If you find *anything* that you don't fully understand and/or have questions about after getting a quote, reading reviews and a sample policy, be sure you get clarification before purchasing a policy.

Watch this video of a pet owner telling about her call to Embrace pet insurance company. http://tinyurl.com/hb42ggj

Step 5 - Choose A Company

By the time you get to this step, you should have it narrowed down to only 2 or 3 companies and more than likely you can't go wrong with any of them. But, consider all you've learned and choose one of them. There is no perfect company - they all have positives and negatives.

Pet insurance companies tweak their policies from time to time and sometimes make wholesale changes. Therefore, including detailed company information in a printed book would soon become obsolete. I've designed two tools to help you navigate through the 5-step research process to select a company to insure your pet:

1) Company Profiles (pdf) - Each company that sells policies in the United States has a section. You'll find helpful details about their policies and links to pages on their website that highlight things that are unique to the company.

For most companies, I've included an audio clip taken from an interview with a representative of the company - oftentimes the Founder and President/CEO of the company explaining details about their policies.

At the end of each company's profile, there is a fillable form with the links you'll need to complete each of the 5 steps and a place to record the information you'll need to objectively compare companies with one another.

As you go through each company's profile and fill out the form, ask yourself these questions:

"What do I like best about this company?"

"What do I not like about this company?"

"What kind of vibes did I get when listening to the audio clip of the company representative or talking with a person at the company when I called with questions?"

Then check "Yes" or "No" to indicate if the company makes the cut for your final consideration.

Watch this video that shows how to use the Company Profiles: http://tinyurl.com/z828lfd

2) Company Comparison Worksheet - an Excel worksheet that allows you to compare companies side-by-side and how they stand on most of the factors I listed earlier in this chapter. It has built-in formulas that calculate your out-of-pocket expense after you enter the premium and whatever policy maximum, deductible and copay you select.

Watch this video demonstrating how to use the Company Comparison Worksheet: http://tinyurl.com/h4m3zlw

If you don't have Excel, you can also use the spreadsheet program Calc in Open Office - a free download at http://openoffice.org. It works in Calc just like it does in Excel.

The Company Profiles and the Company Comparison Worksheet are both available as part of the Pet Insurance Toolkit at:
http://petinsurancetoolkit.com

Choosing A Policy To Insure Your Pet

Most human health insurance policies have a stop-loss feature. You pay the deductible, then a 20% copay up to say $20,000, then the insurance company pays 100% of the bill over $20,000. So, if you have a $1,000 deductible, you know that your maximum out of pocket expense for the year would be $4,800.

Pet insurance doesn't have a stop-loss feature, so you need to ask yourself two questions when designing a policy that will cover your needs:

✓ What is the most I can afford to pay monthly for the premium?

✓ What is the most I can afford to pay out-of-pocket annually for claims?

You need to insure for those costs you cannot afford to pay out-of-pocket. Ideally the goal is to self-insure as much as possible with a pet health savings account. This allows you to pay out-of-pocket for the little stuff. The insurance is to help you pay for those unexpected and larger expenses. If more purchasers of pet insurance adopted this philosophy, I'm convinced that premiums would rise less frequently and more gradually.

So, in addition to purchasing pet insurance, open a savings account that you designate as a pet health savings account. You will use this money to pay for the deductible, copay and any uncovered expenses. You could also use it to save for your pet's wellness care expenses. If you like, you could even use it to pay the insurance premium. If your pet is relatively healthy, money will accumulate in this account.

Your premium will increase with time because of one or more factors (pg. 29), and it may rise to a level you aren't comfortable paying monthly. Having money in the pet health savings account will enable you to pay more out-of-pocket and decrease your premium by downgrading your policy (increase your deductible and/or copay or lower the policy maximum). It's simply a matter of doing the math. Again, look at the guidelines I outlined earlier in the book (pgs. 30-31).

Using the Policy Selection Worksheet I've designed, you should be able to custom design a policy that will give you the lowest out-of-pocket expense (including the annual premium) should you have to file a large claim. The Policy Selection Worksheet is also available as part of the Pet Insurance Toolkit.

Look at this video showing you how to use the worksheet: http://tinyurl.com/znwfvyt

Should You Add Wellness Care Coverage?

Because wellness care is essential to keeping a pet happy and healthy and it is an expected expense every year, I've found that more and more pet owners are expressing an interest in purchasing wellness coverage along with their pet insurance.

Listen to Laura Bennett, CEO of Embrace, explain why they decided to start offer wellness coverage as an option:
http://tinyurl.com/qdqyrjl

When you look at most wellness plans offered by pet insurance companies, you'll discover that you can potentially get back more than you pay for the plan. However, I can assure you that insurance companies don't offer wellness coverage to lose money on it. For example, your pet will only be spayed or neutered once. He will usually only get microchipped once. He won't necessarily get all vaccines every year. And pet owners usually leave some of the potential reimbursements on the table (unused) some years.

Pets Best's plan is an example of a typical wellness package offered by most pet insurance companies. They provide a list of services they consider to be wellness care and a reimbursement amount for each one.
http://tinyurl.com/p8z86y3

Embrace's plan is a different approach in that you can spend your annual allowance however you want. If you want to spend it all on dental care, you can. You aren't limited to a fixed dollar amount for each service included in their wellness package. (http://tinyurl.com/z6owkna

VPI's (Nationwide) new Whole Pet plus Wellness policy covers wellness expenses just like accidents and illnesses subject to your deductible and copay. They also offer a stand-alone pet wellness plan separate from insurance. (http://tinyurl.com/zuxgyq2)

The procedures or vaccines your pet needs in any given year will depend on your pet's age, lifestyle, previous vaccination history, and results of the wellness exam.

Canine core vaccines (rabies, distemper, and parvo) may only be given every 3 years instead of annually. The bordetella (kennel cough) and influenza vaccine may only be needed if your dog is likely to be in a kennel environment for boarding or grooming. The lyme vaccine may only be given in areas of the country where lyme disease is most prevalent.

Feline core vaccines (FVRCP and rabies) may only be given every 3 years. The feline leukemia vaccine is commonly given to kittens, but generally only recommended for adult cats if they are at risk for exposure. The FIP and FIV vaccines are rarely given.

However, a wellness exam once or twice a year, wellness lab testing, certain vaccines, tests for heartworms and intestinal parasites (fecal), heartworm and flea/tick prevention products, and teeth cleaning may be recommended annually.

You should contact your veterinarian to find out what he or she recommends at certain ages (life stages) for your pet and the cost of those services. Then, it comes down to simply doing the math. Add up the reimbursement amounts for all the procedures your pet is likely to require in any given year and subtract the amount you pay for wellness coverage to determine whether you'll come out ahead or not. You may determine that you'll come out ahead by just paying for your pet's wellness care out-of-pocket.

There are some veterinary hospitals who are now offering their own wellness packages that include possibly free office visits and discounts on procedures and products, etc. They will often allow you to pay for it on a monthly payment plan. Banfield has been doing this for years and other hospitals have patterned their plans accordingly. This is not insurance, but simply a wellness plan. Even with these plans, always ask if your pet really needs everything in the plan according to his or her life stage. Then determine if you are likely to come out ahead purchasing it vs. paying out-of-pocket.

Here are some reviews of Banfield. http://tinyurl.com/7wge9ry

Obviously, one of the primary reasons they offer these plans is to bond you to their practice. In other words, the only place you can get these free or discounted services is at that hospital. However, if your pet needs to go to an emergency or specialty hospital, those freebies and discounts won't apply. This is where a pet insurance policy that covers accidents and illnesses that can be used anywhere comes in handy. Wellness plans offered by insurance companies can also usually be used anywhere.

If you do get a wellness plan from your veterinarian or from an insurance company, pay attention to what's included and take advantage of it. Otherwise, you are likely to pay more for the plan than you get out of it.

What About Pre-Existing Conditions?

A pre-existing condition is a problem or disease that your pet may have shown symptoms of or been diagnosed with before the effective date of the policy. Most insurance companies will use the date you first noticed the problem, not necessarily the day it was diagnosed by a veterinarian.

From reading reviews that policyholders write on the various companies, this is a frequently given reason that reimbursement for a claim is denied. How can you avoid this? Buy a policy when you first acquire a puppy or kitten and/or before your pet manifests any signs of illness. After enrolling your pet, there will be a waiting period – usually 24 to 72 hours for accidents and 2 weeks to 1 month (varies depending on the company) for illnesses. If your pet gets sick or injured before you purchase a policy or during this waiting period, it will be considered pre-existing and it is unlikely the condition will be covered. Clients suddenly become interested in pet health insurance when they are in my office and their pet has a serious problem. Unfortunately, that's not the best time to inquire about it.

During the application process, you will usually have to answer several questions about any previous problems your pet may have had. Knowingly misleading the insurance company about your pet's previous problems can lead to the policy to being cancelled.

You will likely be required to send in medical records when you file the first claim. If you have forgotten to mention something during the application process, it may become evident when the company reviews the medical record and a condition could be considered pre-existing and excluded from coverage. You may have just casually mentioned something to your veterinarian that he or she noted in your pet's medical record and could be a signal to the pet insurance company of a potential pre-existing condition whether you considered it to be a big deal or not.

Therefore, you should ask the insurance company as soon as you sign up for a policy if they will conduct a medical record review and let you know in writing if there are any conditions that will be considered pre-existing and excluded from coverage. This is worth asking about so that there aren't any surprises down the road. The last thing you want to do is pay several months/years of premiums only to find out that a claim is denied because the insurance company considers a condition pre-existing before you bought the policy.

Merrick, a reader and guest poster on my blog, switched pet insurance companies when his dog was 10 years old. He asked for a medical record review and wrote about the results. http://tinyurl.com/huxuaxe

Embrace is a company that openly encourages having a medical record review done. Listen to Laura Bennett, Embrace's CEO, explain why: http://tinyurl.com/o9nzdyd

Most companies will do a medical record review if you ask, but they don't do it routinely because it takes up extra time to conduct such a review. Therefore, they don't consider it practical to do on every new application. Neither do veterinarians appreciate their staff's time being used to copy and send medical records to insurance companies. However, I believe it is something you should, at least, attempt to do.

When you receive the results of the review, if one or more conditions are excluded from coverage, you will usually have the option to cancel the policy for a refund of premium as long as you haven't filed a claim. Another benefit of having a medical record review done early on is that when you do file your first claim, any questions about whether a condition is covered can be decided quickly and the reimbursement process will be expedited.

If your pet is older when you apply for a policy, the insurance company may request your pet's medical records to review or even require a physical exam and/or lab testing (at your expense) to make sure your pet doesn't have a chronic condition that would preclude coverage for illnesses. But, don't let this deter you from applying for pet insurance if you have an older pet. As you can see from Merrick's story above, it can be done successfully and over the next several years paid off big time for him.

One subcategory of pre-existing conditions is what most insurance companies call "bilateral conditions." These are problems that occur on one side of the body that are also prone to happen on the opposite side of the body. For example, let's say your dog had a ruptured cruciate ligament in the left hind leg prior to your purchasing a policy. You decide pet insurance would have come in handy helping you pay for such an expense and purchase a policy. Two years later the cruciate ligament in the right hind leg ruptures and needs surgery. But, you discover that it isn't covered because of the bilateral condition exclusion. Therefore, you should read the policy and/or ask about this.

If you feel that a claim was wrongly denied because the company considered a condition pre-existing, you can file an appeal and sometimes the decision can be overturned in your favor resulting in the company paying the claim. Some companies have several levels of appeal. The first level might be a veterinarian on their staff who contacts your veterinarian to get more information. If your claim is denied again, the next level might be one or more veterinarians (sometimes specialists) who are independent of the company who will review the case and render a judgement. Your policy should explain how appeals are handled.

There are often "gray areas" when deciding if a condition is pre-existing. For example, is the current episode of diarrhea related to an episode that occurred before you purchased insurance? Unless the cause of the diarrhea in either case is specifically known, it may be impossible to say for sure. I believe that's when common sense should prevail. Ideally, a decision to call a condition pre-existing should also be supportable by current evidence-based medical knowledge.

As mentioned earlier, when you are doing your research and reading reviews, be sure to look at the negative reviews. Do you see a recurring trend that a company denies a lot of claims because of pre-existing conditions? Look at the comments following these reviews. Is there are response from the insurer that might shed more light on the reason for denial? Does their explanation make sense? Was the claim rightfully denied for a reason that obviously wasn't a "gray area" situation? A frequent example of this is when a condition occurs after signing up for a policy, but during the waiting period before the policy to become effective.

In this chapter, I've talked about 3 ways to minimize potential frustrations regarding having a claim denied because of pre-existing conditions:

1) Carefully screen companies before purchase in favor of those who tend to pay vs. deny claims in the "gray area" situations. Does a company seem to give the policyholder the benefit of the doubt and find a reason to pay the claim vs. deny the claim?

2) After signing up for a policy, request a medical record review.

3) If you sincerely believe a claim was wrongly denied, file an appeal to see if you can get the decision overturned in your favor and the claim paid.

Filing A Claim

You can usually download a claim form from the company's website. Some claim forms require a veterinarian's signature, but many of them nowadays don't.

Read your policy for specific instructions on what the company requires to process a claim. If you have any questions about the requirements, call the company to clarify. Most companies require a claim to be filed within a certain period of time after treatment for a condition - typically 90 - 180 days (should be stated in your policy).

Determine the best way to send in the claim and related documents. Some companies now have Apps to simplify the process. You can take a picture of the invoice and medical record related to the claim and email it to the company. This usually provides the surest and fastest means of filing a claim and receiving reimbursement - especially if the company does direct deposit into your bank account.

Some companies allow you to scan the documents and file a claim online, email them, fax or send via regular (snail) mail.

Some companies will email, text or call you when they receive the claim to let you know the claim is being processed. If you haven't heard back from the company within a reasonable period of time, call to make sure they received the claim and don't need anymore information.

I've seen this statement repeated over and over when reading reviews, "I sent them the claim, but they say they never received it or that they need more information from my veterinarian." When there is a delay in reimbursement, the most common reasons are:

- ✓ Claim form not completely filled out or signed
- ✓ Paid invoice not included with claim form
- ✓ Medical record not included with claim form
- ✓ More information needed

If you have already sent in your pet's medical record for review or with a previous claim, you'll usually only have to send in the medical notes pertaining to the current claim.

There may be times when your pet is faced with a condition requiring hospitalization and/or surgery - a potential big expense. If it's not an emergency and you can wait several days before the procedure is done (e.g. surgery to repair a torn cruciate ligament), it may be wise to contact the company about pre-certifying coverage for the procedure. Your veterinarian will usually need to provide the company with a treatment plan and estimate.

Beware of Managed Care

If you were to ask doctors, dentists, or pharmacists how they feel about "managed care" for human patients, most will tell you they don't like it. In fact, a few will tell you that they have been frustrated enough with managed care to consider giving up their medical careers or to refuse to take patients with insurance or Medicare, etc. If you have medical insurance for yourself or your family, you may not know what managed care is, but you are likely familiar with the terms HMO, PPO, Medicaid, Medicare, in-network, out-of-network, etc. Perhaps you have also experienced frustrations with the current human health insurance industry.

Here are some of the characteristics of managed care:

✓ Health care providers (doctors, dentist, pharmacies, hospitals, etc.) join a network that sets fees at which the providers will be reimbursed in exchange for patients who are part of the network.

✓ The patient's choice of doctors, dentists, hospitals and pharmacies is limited to those who are in the network. If they decide to go to a provider "out-of-network," they are penalized by having to pay a higher portion of the bill. Doctors in a managed care environment aren't necessarily inclined to have a strong doctor-patient relationship because their patients are provided for them by the network.

✓ There may be a time consuming process with layers of bureaucracy in order to receive payment. It can take weeks to months to receive reimbursements from the insurance company. Most providers have separate departments just to handle insurance claims and billing. This increases the costs of providing medical care.

✓ Sometimes the decisions about appropriate diagnostic tests and treatment are taken away from the doctor actually seeing the patient and made by an employee of the network in another city. This can be detrimental to quality healthcare.

I recently had dinner with an elderly couple. The husband has several major medical problems. He is diabetic and has an insulin pump for which he has to order supplies to keep it working. He said that Medicare is refusing to pay for any more supplies saying that he no longer needs it. This is despite his doctor and two endocrinologists saying that he does. His comment to me was, "I think they just want me to go ahead and die so they won't have to pay any more medical costs for me."

Pet health insurance differs from human health insurance today in that there aren't well-established HMOs or PPOs. This is considered an advantage for pet owners since they aren't required to go to a particular doctor or hospital in a "network." They can go to any veterinarian, emergency center, or specialist and their insurance company will reimburse them for part of the costs.

When thinking about the current state of pet health insurance vs. managed care, it is likely that:

Clients want:

✓ To choose their own veterinarian

✓ Insurance that is easy to understand and provides high reimbursements

✓ Fast claim payment with no hassle

✓ The option to have routine wellness procedures covered

✓ Few exclusions/limitations

✓ Affordable premiums

Veterinarians want:

✓ The ability for the client and treating doctor to determine the level of care - no third party dictating the quality of care (disallowing diagnostic or treatment recommendations of the treating doctor).

✓ Little or no paperwork in filing claims

✓ No contractual schedule of fees or benefits dictating or implying what to charge. Individual practices must have the freedom to set fees that suit the style and level of care that they provide their clients and patients

✓ Clients who are able to choose where to take their pet for care including specialists

It seems that every other healthcare field has eventually gravitated away from a fee-for-service insurance toward managed care. If pet owners (who seek healthcare for their pets) and veterinarians (who provide the healthcare for pets) want to keep the freedoms and choices they now enjoy with pet health insurance as it is, then both must diligently resist any drift toward managed care. This is best done when neither of them joins a network that would limit the pet owner's choice of veterinarian or that would dictate what level of care the veterinarian could provide and the reimbursements he or she would receive for doing so.

Pet Assure is a company (club) that has a network of participating veterinary hospitals that offer their services at a discount (25%) to members of the club. Usually, the pet owner pays an annual membership fee to belong to this club and be eligible for the discounts. They offer annual memberships for individual dogs or cats as well as family plans that cover multiple pets. It is not insurance. There are no deductibles or co-pays. Pre-existing, hereditary, and chronic conditions are eligible for the discount. You receive the discount when paying your bill at the veterinarian's office.

Services and products that aren't eligible for a discount usually include any medication you are sent home with, food, flea and tick or heartworm preventatives, boarding or grooming, outside lab tests, referral to a specialist, and any product or procedure that is already discounted.

The main problem with a network such as this is that it requires the veterinarian/hospital to discount their services. Therefore, there are often a very limited number of veterinarians participating in a given city or community. In other words, the veterinarian that you prefer and have an established relationship with may not be willing to participate in such a network.

Even though this isn't insurance, it has some of the characteristics of "managed care." It requires veterinarians to join a network and discount their services in return for clients who are members of the network.

Pet Assure website: http://petassure.com

Read the reviews on Pet Assure compared to insurance companies. http://tinyurl.com/zjlm33f

The Future of Pet Insurance

Pet insurance has been available in this country since 1982 and yet only 1% - 2% of pets in the U.S are insured. The current model of pet insurance in the U.S. is one of reimbursement - that is, the pet owner pays the veterinarian in full and then seeks reimbursement from the insurance company.

I believe there are pet owners who want the best for their pet and can afford a monthly premium, a deductible and co-pay, but would have trouble coming up with thousands of dollars out-of-pocket (cash or credit) if their pet had a major illness or injury. Therefore, it seems that there are potentially many pet owners and their pets who aren't able to benefit from pet insurance as it is presently structured.

Some of the pet insurance companies have provisions in their policies to reimburse the veterinary hospital directly if the veterinarian will agree to such an arrangement. The pet owner would still have to pay the veterinary hospital the deductible, co-pay, and for any non-covered expenses.

The veterinary community is very reluctant to start accepting reimbursements from pet insurance companies. Many fear it may be a first step down the pathway to managed care. For these attitudes to change and potentially more pets to benefit from pet insurance coverage, the following will have to be addressed by pet insurance companies:

- ✓ A fast and reliable method of pre-certification. In other words, there must be a way to determine quickly on the front end whether a claim is covered and how much will be reimbursed.

- ✓ There must be a fast (likely electronic and preferably paperless) way to file claims and receive reimbursements.

- ✓ Can pre-certification, filing a claim, and receiving reimbursement be done in *real time* or close to it?

Some individual companies are already capable of doing this.

By reading your policy, you should know what is and isn't covered, and if you've had a medical records review done, you should know if there are any pre-existing conditions that aren't covered. So, ask your insurance company what's involved in getting pre-certification done and how quickly you or your veterinarian will be reimbursed when a claim is filed.

In my opinion, for pet insurance to work more effectively for policyholders and veterinary hospitals, the following should be a reality:

Pet insurance companies should be available 24 hours a day - 365 days of the year to provide quick pre-certification of potential claims. Ironically, emergency visits often occur at hours when most pet insurance companies aren't available for consultation. This is unfortunate because these are the very times and situations when decisions are made by pet owners about whether to proceed with treatment or sadly even euthanize their pet when they can't pay the large deposit or estimated total bill up front – even if they have insurance.

Ideally, the pet owner and a veterinary hospital should have available to them how much of the deductible has been met for the policy year as well as the balance of the per-incident or annual limit left for the policy year. This type of policy information should be available 24/7 on the pet insurance company's website and easily accessible with a cell phone. Perhaps even a claim/reimbursement calculator could be available.

Another need is affordable coverage for policyholders who have multiple pets. Even though most companies offer discounts when multiple pets are insured, it can still be cost prohibitive for many pet owners. Petfirst offers a "family plan" where multiple pets share an annual maximum, but each pet has it's own deductible, etc. Perhaps other companies can design affordable family pet insurance plans?

Over the past 5 or 6 years, virtually all the companies have "tweaked" their policies in an attempt to remain competitive and/or gain an advantage in the industry. They've changed deductibles, co-pays, added coverage for hereditary or chronic conditions, etc. But, policies can be tweaked only so much and still only 1 to 2 percent of pets in the United States are covered by insurance.

So, here's the challenge - who's going to figure out how to reach those pet owners and their pets who aren't currently able to benefit from pet insurance? With this question in mind, I would ask that the pet insurance community and the veterinary community consider the following statements:

"What do I believe is impossible to do in my field, but if it could be done would fundamentally change my business?"
Joel Barker - Paradigms

"To reach people nobody else is reaching, we must do what nobody else is doing." -- Craig Groeschel

"The next generation product almost never comes from the previous generation." --Al Ries - Focus

---

Trupanion *has* stepped up to the plate spending millions of dollars developing Trupanion Express to replace the reimbursement model. It allows Trupanion to pay the veterinarian directly often in real time - the same day services are provided for the client. I believe this is an example of "thinking outside the box" that is required to move pet insurance forward and allow more and more pets to be insured which ultimately will save lives. Although they have done a good job of designing the product to minimize the time required for pre-certification, filing the claim and receiving reimbursement, it does rely on the training and involvement/interaction of the veterinary hospital staff with the pet insurance company claims department - potentially multiple times a day. Despite this, the veterinarians I've talked to who are using Trupanion Express feel it has had a positive impact on their practice - even those who were skeptical at first.

Will other companies come up with their own innovative solution that makes it easier for more pet owners to experience the benefits of pet insurance? The veterinary community in general (and insurance companies are aware of this), would prefer a solution that would very minimally involve veterinary staff time and the need for veterinarians to receive direct payment from the insurance company.

Listen to this discussion with Dr. Fran Wilkerson:
http://tinyurl.com/hl6h8wx

Listen as Dr. Jules Benson at Petplan idscusses managed care: (http://tinyurl.com/gq8nlof)

Conduct An Annual Policy Checkup

You've probably gotten a card, letter, or email from your insurance agent recommending a checkup (review) of all your insurances (auto, homeowners, life, etc.) to see if your situation has changed in any way that would indicate a change in your coverage is necessary.

Every year, about a month or so before your pet insurance policy renewal date, you'll receive a notice from the insurance company informing you of any policy changes and also whether your premium will change.

This is an excellent time to conduct your own annual pet insurance policy checkup. Doing such a checkup will force you to become more familiar with your policy (a good thing) and also alert you to any needed changes in your coverage. To facilitate this review, I recommend keeping a file folder that contains all your veterinary invoices, claim forms, benefit/reimbursement statements, and of course, your insurance policy.

Here are some things to consider when doing an annual pet insurance policy checkup:

✓ If you filed one or more claims, was the reimbursement less than you expected? Were there specific items/procedures on the receipt you submitted with a claim that wasn't covered and this caught you by surprise? Perhaps you received *no* reimbursement (claim was denied). Do you know why? If not, find out by reading the Explanation of Benefits (EOB) associated with that claim and/or call the insurance company. This may also be an indication you need to become more familiar with your policy. Read some reviews for your company (http://petinsurancereview.com). Is there a recurring theme from other pet owners of having claims denied for similar reasons? Any complaints about receiving lower than expected reimbursements?

✓ Was the length of time to receive reimbursement satisfactory?

✓ If the company has come out with new policy options since your last renewal, do they better fit your needs? Call the company to get more details and ask if you qualify to take advantages of these changes. Get a company representative to explain the positives and negatives of making any changes you are considering in light of your present coverage. Anytime you make any changes to your policy (switch policies, change your annual or per-incident maximum, change your deductible or copay, add/drop a rider or endorsement) – make sure you understand the ramifications of doing so. Especially consider how any conditions for which your pet has been previously diagnosed and treated will be handled after such changes are made.

✓ Do you have wellness care coverage? If so, did you come out ahead this year? Compare your reimbursements for wellness procedures with the amount you paid in extra premium to have them covered. Were there wellness procedures that were covered that you could/should have had done, but you didn't (you left money on the table)? Why?

If you don't have wellness coverage and the company offers it, should you consider getting it? Read previous chapter on page 51.

If you have wellness coverage and drop it, will it adversely affect your coverage for accidents and illness in any way? If you drop it, can you get it again in the future if you want it again?

✓ Has your premium increased out of your comfort zone (budget)? If so, follow the advice given previously on pages 30-31.

✓ Should you consider switching pet insurance companies? Unless you realize you made a truly unwise choice when you selected the company you have now, first consider looking at available options to improve the coverage you have with your current company. Call the company and discuss any concerns you have.

If you are considering switching companies, consider using the Pet Insurance Toolkit (http://petinsurancetoolkit.com) to do a re-evaluation of all the companies. New companies may have entered the market or one or more companies may have changed their policies since you last bought a policy. Can you get better coverage for less money with another company?

However, realize that any conditions your pet has been diagnosed and treated for will likely be considered pre-existing with a new company. If you apply with a new company, have them conduct a medical record review and let you know what conditions will be considered pre-existing and not covered before dropping your old policy. This may affect your decision whether to switch companies or not - especially if your pet has one or more chronic conditions that *are* covered under your present policy. See page 56 for a link to Merrick's guest blog post entitled "Switching Companies in Midstream."

✓ Has your pet been spayed or neutered since you bought a policy? If so, you may be eligible for a discount. Call the company and see if you qualify for this or any other discounts?

Conducting an annual pet insurance policy checkup will often give you a better understanding of the coverage that you have and hopefully improve your coverage while keeping your premium affordable.

Resources

After reading this book, you should be able to answer these three questions:

1) Should I purchase pet insurance?
2) How does it work?
3) Which company and policy is best for my pet?

I would sincerely appreciate it if you took just a moment to email me (http://tinyurl.com/j2novsm) and let me know if I was successful in achieving these goals.

Even if you just have some questions, I'll do my best to help you. I would love to start a conversation because I also learn from you. Each person's situation or experience with pet insurance is a little different.

For those who write me with feedback on this book, I'll send you a link to download "The Wise Pet Owner: How To Save Money On Your Pet's Heathcare." It's great to have pet insurance when the unexpected happens, but it's even better to prevent problems from happening in the first place. As Ben Franklin once said, "An ounce of prevention is worth a pound of cure."

As a practicing veterinarian, I decided to write The Wise Pet Owner after observing that many of the injuries and illnesses I kept seeing over and over could have been easily and inexpensively prevented - saving pets from needless suffering and clients potentially thousands of dollars.

"The Wise Pet Owner is the book I have been writing in my head for years, but if too many people read it, it could put us out of business. The material it covers should be mandatory reading for everyone prior to getting a pet." – C. Atkinson, Administrator, Animal Emergency Center, Memphis, TN.

Additional resources available to you:

Your Pet Insurance Guide Blog
(http://petinsuranceguideus.com)

Pet Insurance Guide Podcast
(http://petinsuranceguidepodcast.com)

Pet Insurance Toolkit
(http://petinsurancetoolkit.com)

A collegue, Dr. Fran Wilkerson, who was
referenced several times in this book has
a very helpful website that has a lot of
company information in a table format
at Pet Insurance University.
(http://pet-insurance-university.com)

Thanks for reading this book and it is my sincere hope that you've
learned some things you didn't know and you've benefited from the
information. If so, please consider leaving a review on the site you
purchased the book - it is greatly appreciated!

Also, please spread the word about the book to any of your friends,
neighbors, or family members who have pets - and *even your veterinarian*!

CPSIA information can be obtained
at www.ICGtesting.com
Printed in the USA
LVHW071702201118
597790LV00020B/215/P

9 780982 322147